Date Due			
JUL 7			

LEGENDS OF THE SAINTS

Legends of the Saints

by E. LUCIA TURNBULL

illustrations by
LILI RETHI

Philadelphia
J. B. Lippincott Company
New York

PRINTED IN THE UNITED STATES OF AMERICA

LIBRARY OF CONGRESS CATALOG CARD NUMBER: 59-9219

CONTENTS

LEGENDS OF THE SAINTS

 GENTLE LION

Night comes quickly in the desert. The sun sets, and almost at once the sky is sparkling with stars. Then, after the burning heat of the day, the air is cooler. It was at this hour that St. Jerome came out of his cell to read evening prayers with his monks in the cloisters. Each Brother had brought with him a little lamp, which he had carefully trimmed and filled with oil, and the light of these lamps cast a circle of brightness and showed up the broad entry of the monastery gates. By St. Jerome's orders these gates always stood open, "For," said he, "some weary traveler may come this way and ask for sanctuary."

But there were those among the Brothers who would have liked to have the gates closed as night fell, for it was then that the wild animals began their prowl in search of food, or came to drink, for the monastery was built close

I

to the River Nile. But when they spoke of this to their Abbot, he bade them be of braver heart, and the gates stood open.

The reading of the lesson had just begun, when a shadow fell across the circle of light and a full-grown lion came limping through the gates. With a cry of terror the Brothers dropped their books and fled into the monastery, only two hanging back a little, not liking to leave St. Jerome alone. On came the lion, on three legs only, holding up one paw as if in pain. And towards the great beast went St. Jerome, with as good a smile of welcome as if the visitor had been a needy man.

"See," he said to the two monks who were watching fearfully from the shadows, "this poor beast is in great pain. Look how he shows us his injured paw. Go quickly and get me a basin, water, and the healing herbs I use for all hurts. Then I will see what ails the lion. And be very sure he will do no harm to any of us."

The lion stood drooping before the Saint, the useless paw held up, almost in supplication.

"Ah, poor creature," said St. Jerome, "if you could speak you would tell me how you came to be in this plight." And he stroked the lion's mane, while the lion looked at him trustfully.

When the monks brought the remedies, St. Jerome bathed the paw and found that it was pierced by a great

2

thorn. This he drew out skilfully, and dressed the wound with care. And the lion, as if knowing that he was amongst friends and safe there, did not depart into the desert when the paw was healed, but remained at the monastery, tame and gentle as a faithful dog.

"Verily, I believe that this lion wishes to be useful to us," said St. Jerome, when he saw the lion did not go. "Now I wonder if we could find some work for him, for no one is ever idle here."

Then, an old monk, one wise in the ways of animals, replied, "You know, Father, that we have been anxious for a long time about the donkey who goes to bring our wood. Whenever he is late, we fear some accident has happened to the good creature, that he has been stolen, or that a wild beast has devoured him. Now if this grateful lion took care of the donkey, and brought him back safely every day, we should have no fear for our old friend, and the lion would be earning his place here."

"I like that idea," said St. Jerome, and calling the lion to him, he said slowly, "Will you, my friend, go out daily with the donkey and see he comes to no harm?"

The lion seemed to understand what was asked of him, and when the donkey went out the next morning, paced beside him. And this went on for a long time, the lion never failing to bring the donkey and his load of wood safely home.

3

But one day, overcome by the great heat, the lion lay down in the shade of a palm tree, and while the donkey grazed, fell asleep. It was then that a party of merchants came along on their way into Egypt to buy oil. And seeing the donkey, but not the sleeping lion, they said amongst themselves, "Why, there is a stray donkey. Why shouldn't we add him to our train?"

So the donkey was seized, and a camel's halter put round his neck, after which he was led off by the merchants, who were soon lost to sight in the cloud of sand which rose up behind them.

A little later the lion woke up and, stretching himself, got up and went to look for the donkey. But he was nowhere in sight. In great distress the lion galloped this way and that, roaring dismally. And this went on for the whole of the day. It was long past the time due for the lion and the donkey to return to the monastery, when St. Jerome asked, "Did any of you hear a lion roaring? I hope nothing has happened to upset our good friend."

Most of the Brothers had heard the noise, and all were getting anxious about the fate of the donkey.

"I will go a little way beyond the gates and see if they are coming," said St. Jerome, and, taking up his staff, he set off to look for the missing pair. And there, just outside the monastery gate stood the lion in great dejection, but no donkey was to be seen.

4

"If you could speak," said St. Jerome, to the unhappy creature, "you could tell us what has happened today. But I much fear you may have been overcome by hunger, and eaten the good donkey who was your care."

The lion gave a great sigh, and a Brother, running out to see if the Saint was in danger, cried, "There is no doubt about it. The wicked lion has torn our good donkey to bits and devoured him."

"Well, I thought that at first," replied St. Jerome, "but why should the lion come back here if that was so? Let us be charitable and kind to all things. The lion shall remain here if he will, and do not jibe at him or nag him. If he could speak, he might tell us a strange tale."

Then the old monk who was wise in the ways of animals put in a word, "I think with you, Father," he said, "but it is going to be difficult for us to manage without the donkey, who every day hauled our wood. If the lion wishes to remain here with us, it might be well to let him do the donkey's work, since he took so little care of the poor creature."

"It's a shabby task for a lion," replied St. Jerome thoughtfully, "and yet I see no better way. So put a light harness on him and set him in the way of bringing in the wood we need."

And this was done. Every day the lion brought in the wood, just as the donkey had done. And every day he

5

made a fresh search for his missing friend. But none of the monastery Brothers knew of this, for what man may know the mind of a lion?

Now it happened one day, just as the sun was near setting, that in his search for the vanished donkey, the lion climbed a little slope that overlooked the caravan road, and in the distance he saw a great cloud of dust, which meant that a big company of men and beasts were approaching. The lion, the color of the sand, lay waiting until there came into sight a long line of camels with their drivers, and in front of them a donkey, who, as was the custom, wore a halter like the camels and led them on their way.

Not sure, at first, that this was his own donkey, the lion crouched like a figure of yellow stone, flat against the sand. But as the merchants with their beasts came nearer, he saw that it was his old friend.

With a roar the lion leapt down upon the cavalcade, which sent the merchants flying in terror the way they had come. Leaving all they had behind them, they ran as fast as they could over the soft sand. But the camels, following the donkey, stampeded towards the monastery, the lion coming up behind them, still roaring, but now with joy.

When this astonishing sight met the eyes of St. Jerome and the Brothers, the Saint said, "We did ill to misjudge our lion. He has rewarded good for evil. But I fear he has, in his simplicity, brought to us beasts and goods which are

not ours. However, unload the camels, give them food and drink. Then let us wait and see what happens."

Now, seeing that he had brought the donkey safely home, the lion was once more in good spirits. Going from Brother to Brother, he wagged his tail and did all he could to recover their good opinion. And they, deeply ashamed of their suspicions, patted and praised him all day long.

But St. Jerome said, "If I am not mistaken, the owners of the camels and the rich load they carried will come in search of their lost property. Make ready for a number of guests, for I wish to receive them in a fitting manner."

But this astonished the Brothers.

"Father," said one, "surely you would not treat these thieves as honored guests! Remember it was they who stole our donkey."

"And brought our gentle lion into great trouble," added another.

"I remember that," replied St. Jerome quietly; "all the same, things shall be as I say."

And as he had expected, the merchants, having recovered from their fright when the lion was no longer to be seen, arrived, and being admitted to the monastery, fell upon their knees before St. Jerome, humbly asking him to forgive them for the theft of the donkey.

"It is the lion from whom you should seek forgiveness," said the Saint, smiling, "for it was he who suffered most when you took what did not belong to you. But he is here, and I will summon him, and you may make your peace with him."

At this all the merchants began to tremble, and one, the leader, begged that the noble lion should not be troubled and that they might go quietly away, asking no more of anyone.

"Oh, but you shall take with you your goods, and the camels who brought them here of their own accord," replied St. Jerome. "Only the donkey knew his own home."

Then the merchants, seeing how wrongly they had behaved in stealing the donkey, asked the Saint to accept from them half the oil which the camels carried.

"We are not without oil," said St. Jerome, "and so need not take any toll of your property."

But the merchants said that they would not touch one drop of water, nor yet one morsel of food, unless the good Saint would accept not only half the oil they now carried, but the same amount every year. And this they begged, so that the little lamps of the monastery should never go out, nor yet that great light of love, which St. Jerome had kindled in that land.

And so it was settled, and the merchants went on their way, while the lion and the donkey took up their friendly life again together.

9

CROM DUV'S SUNDAY

THERE is a certain day, the last Sunday in July, when a band of pilgrims go to Croagh Patrick in County Mayo, and a great festival is held on the same day in a place called Mannin amidst the Twelve Pin Mountains in Connemara. This is called Crom Duv's Sunday, and the reason it is so named is because of something which happened a long time ago.

St. Patrick, the Patron Saint of Ireland, was much beloved during his lifetime in that land, even by those who had not yet become Christians, for he was the friend of all men.

And so it came about that the Chieftain of Connaught, called Crom Duv, having slaughtered an ox, wished to send a quarter of the meat to the Saint as a present. So, by his orders, a messenger boy took this with a greeting from his master.

When the boy arrived at the place where St. Patrick was living with his brethren, he found the holy man at his devotions, and so he waited until the Saint came out to him, and then presented the gift.

Now at this time food was very scarce in Ireland, and meat was never seen except on the tables of the rich. Indeed, St. Patrick and his brethren were often hungry, for they depended for most of their food upon the charity of the folk around them, from whom they accepted only enough to live. Therefore, when the Saint saw the generous portion of meat which Crom Duv had sent him, he raised his eyes to Heaven and, blessing the meat, said, "Deo Gratias," which means, "Thanks be to God."

But the messenger, seeing the size of his master's gift, waited for further thanks than just two words. None came, for St. Patrick had returned to his prayers.

The boy went back to his master, who at once asked what thanks the Saint had given for the present.

"Well now, your Honor," replied the boy, "and it was not more than two words the cleric had for it. And I not knowing what they meant because I had never heard them before. So it's little enough thanks I bring you for the grand portion you sent to this Patrick. Enough to feed a dozen hungry men for a week, so it was."

"Do you mean to tell me that I only get two words of thanks for the quarter of an ox?" cried Crom Duv, in a roaring temper. "Maybe this miserable Patrick thought my gift too small. Go back with yet another quarter of the ox. Say it is a further gift from me, Crom Duv, Chieftain of Connaught. Then come back quickly and tell me what he said."

So the boy shouldered another quarter of the ox and, staggering under the load, dropped it at the feet of St. Patrick where he sat, reading from his missal, under a tree.

The Saint looked up, and seeing the same boy, and yet another big portion of meat, was very pleased, because he had given the first lot to the poor. So again he blessed the gift, saying, "Deo Gratias," and that was all.

But the boy, almost afraid to go back to Crom Duv with only this short message of thanks, waited in the hope of something more. But, again, nothing came. And so he had to return and tell the Chieftain what had happened.

"Deo Gratias!" shouted Crom Duv; "even if I knew what the words meant, they are a very poor way of thanking me for such a noble gift. But I will test this Patrick just once more, and if he does not show a proper gratitude for my presents, I shall know what to do with him."

Once more the boy was sent, this time bearing a third quarter of the ox. He found St. Patrick listening to the song of the birds.

Placing the third quarter of the ox before the Saint, the messenger waited for what he felt sure must be a fine message of thanks. But again all he got was just those two words, "Deo Gratias," which he did not understand. Not another sound did St. Patrick utter, but his face, as he lifted it again to hear the song of the birds, was very bright and sweet.

So the boy had to go back, knowing very well that trouble would certainly come from St. Patrick's brief message.

"Well, what kind of thanks do you bring me this time?" growled Crom Duv, his hand upon his sword.

"Ah now, your Honor," replied the boy, almost weeping, "is it my fault that the man yonder can speak only two words? 'Deo Gratias' the first time; 'Deo Gratias' the second time; and even for the third quarter of the ox you sent him—'Deo Gratias' again!"

"Will you listen to that!" roared Crom Duv, in a terrible passion. "And he the biggest talker in all Ireland! Is it to put a slight on me he tosses back only two words in exchange for three quarters of an ox, and he living on the bounty of my people? Run, boy, run your swiftest and tell Patrick that Crom Duv, Chieftain of Connaught, wishes to see him at once!"

And the boy fled, seeing murder in his master's eye.

"Why, you are back again!" said the Saint, as the messenger came up for the fourth time, but on this occasion empty-handed.

Then the boy gave St. Patrick the message from Crom Duv. "And I beg of you to come quickly," he urged, "for I left my master in a very angry mood."

"Why should I delay?" asked the Saint. "And why should your master be angry? Has he not all things but one—and that the greatest of all? This I am ready to give him."

And so St. Patrick went very willingly to visit one who he thought was his friend. Even the angry look—the drawn sword—of Crom Duv did not affright him.

"You sent for me?" he asked quietly.

But Crom Duv burst out furiously, "What kind of gratitude have you shown me for the three quarters of a fine ox I sent you?"

"Very deep gratitude," replied the Saint, in the same quiet voice as before.

"Two words only of thanks—and those words I did not understand!" stormed the angry Chief.

"But those two words carried my very best thanks," explained St. Patrick, "thanks I could not have sent you in a finer way."

"Do you know what the meat I sent you weighed?" cried Crom Duv, still flaming with rage.

"Do *you* know what my thanks weighed?" asked the Saint, not angry at all. "Have you any scales, Crom Duv?"

"I have," replied Crom Duv, with a scowl.

"Then let them be brought," said St. Patrick, calmly. When the scales were produced he added, "Have you, also, three quarters of an ox equal in weight and quality to the three you sent me?"

"I have," was the surly answer.

"Then let those also be brought," said St. Patrick, and while they stood there waiting for the meat, the Saint wrote the words "Deo Gratias" three times on a piece of parchment.

"Now," he continued, when the meat was carried in, "place the three quarters of the ox on one of the scales. On the other I will put this parchment, and we shall then know which was the greater—your gift or my thanks."

Anxiously Crom Duv watched the weighing of the meat against the piece of parchment, and when the latter tipped the scales right down, all the anger faded from his face to give place to wonder.

Falling upon his knees before the Saint, he cried, "Oh, most blessed and holy Patrick! Tell me the meaning of those two words which, written on a flimsy scrap of parchment, outweigh my gift of three quarters of an ox."

"Listen, my friend," said St. Patrick, placing a hand upon the Chief's bent head, "those two words are forever blessed—'Deo Gratias,' which means 'God be thanked.'"

And he raised Crom Duv from his knees.

Then was Crom Duv converted, he and all his people,

and baptized into the Christian faith by St. Patrick, the Patron Saint of Ireland. And from that day the last Sunday of July has always been known in those parts as "Crom Duv's Sunday."

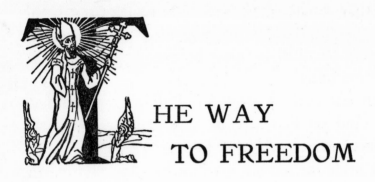

THE WAY
TO FREEDOM

In the north of Ireland—which is known as Ulster—stands a hill called Slemish. It is a green hill and a famous one, for on its slopes—more than fourteen hundred years ago—St. Patrick spent seven years of slavery minding his master's sheep and swine.

He had been seized and carried off from the coast of Wales by pirates, and sold to Milchu, an Ulster Chief, who, if rough and savage in his ways, was not cruel to Patrick, so far as we know.

If the slave boy had been really unhappy in Ireland, he would not have come to love the country and its people so much. Nor would he have wished to return there. But he did, and became Ireland's first Christian Bishop, and Patron Saint of the land which he had first seen as a slave.

But a slave could never have done all the things which

this great Christian accomplished, nor could he have learned those lessons which made Patrick such a wonderful teacher. And so, because he must have felt that to do God's work on earth he must be free, he made up his mind to run away.

It was not easy. A slave has little money and few friends. And yet Patrick must have had a little money and a few friends, or he could not have got away as he did, nor made the journey even on foot over very rough country to the distant port of Inver Dea—near to Dublin and two hundred Irish miles away.

In those days there were no buses or country-carts, and a slave would never ride on a horse. Even a donkey would be too grand a mount for him. Besides, Patrick wanted to set out upon this great adventure as secretly as possible. And so he left his hut on the hillside at the dead of night and made his way down the trackless slopes of Slemish until he reached the valley and struck out for the South.

It was still dark, but a twittering of the birds showed that dawn was approaching, and to the East a faint gleam meant that the sun was rising behind the distant hills.

From a little cabin a wisp of blue smoke curled towards the sky. Someone had lit a turf fire. As Patrick slipped past, the door of the cabin opened and an old crone peered out, then seeing the boy called out in friendship, "A hundred thousand welcomes to ye! You're early on the road."

"I've a long way to go," replied Patrick truthfully. He hoped the old woman did not recognize him as a runaway slave.

"Come in, come in," she invited kindly. "I've a drop of buttermilk and a piece of bread ready and waiting for you."

And Patrick, who had little enough food in his bundle, was glad indeed to step in and break his fast.

The old woman lived quite alone. She was more than a hundred years old, she said, and had none of her own kith and kin living at all.

"And where is your journey's end?" she asked him, as he drank the milk and ate the sliver of rough bread.

"I am going to Inver Dea," he told her, "for there is news of a ship sailing from there in a few days' time."

"Mercy on us!" she cried, "and that's the dangerous road to travel! Why, stranger, there's a bog or two more than a mile wide between this and there. Only those who know it are sure to cross in safety. Now will you turn back, or see if a fisherman will take you across Lough Neagh?"

"I must make the journey quite alone," replied Patrick, and he rose from the little creepie-stool, and held out his hand.

The old woman took it in her skinny paw, and looking at him very earnestly said, "When you come to the place where the bog is, you may find a child waiting to guide you across—a child wearing a rag of a red dress, with hair like a black cloak about her. Follow the child, and you will come to no harm."

"And with what shall I reward her?" asked Patrick, for he had little enough to give away.

"Be off with you," cried the old woman, giving him a friendly push. "We don't sell our goodwill in Ireland!"

And she would take nothing for the breakfast of bread and milk she had given him. He turned back to wave to her as the road took a bend round a wood. She was watching him, shading her eyes with her hand against the bright rays of the rising sun.

Patrick went on, feeling much cheered by all this kindness, and it seemed to him that the hardest part of his journey was over when he came to the wide bog of which the old woman had told him. For as far as he could see, the moss and heather stretched like a green-and-purple sea. And well he knew that almost as deep as a sea it might be—for both moss and heather grew on a great depth of mud. A track across the bog there would be for those who knew it.

He paused and looked about him. And then he saw the child. She was just as the old woman had described her; wearing a rag of a red dress with her black hair like a cloak around her. Her eyes, large and of the darkest blue, were fixed upon him. But all she said was, "Come! Mark my footsteps. Tread in them boldly."

And then she set off ahead of him, singing under her breath as children do when they are out of doors and happy. When she had led him safely across, and they were on the firm ground the other side of the bog, she said gently, "And when you come back I shall be waiting for you, even if it should be after many days."

"I will come back, I will most certainly come back," promised Patrick; "if it is only to thank you again for guiding me over the bog. And I would like you to take this to remember me by."

Then, from a cord which he wore round his neck, he took a little silver Cross and put it into her hand.

"I have never seen anything like this before," she whispered, and her eyes shone like blue jewels.

"Keep it in remembrance of me," said Patrick. "And now I must go on and you must go back. God be with you!"

"And with you," she replied, and stood watching him, as the old woman had done, until he was gone from her sight.

Patrick now went on alone, as he must for many days. But at last he came to the port of Inver Dea, and there, as he had expected, a ship was waiting. The weather had broken and the wind blew hard. Outside the little harbor

great waves piled up crested with white foam.

The captain of the ship was taking a pack of Irish hounds over to France, where such dogs were greatly valued, but his crew had no wish to start in such weather, and the dogs were half wild with terror, leashed on short leads and held by strange men.

Patrick, in whom the love of all animals was as strong as his love of children, went forward to speak with the captain—to ask him if he could work a passage on the ship.

"That you may not!" snapped the captain, in a rage with wind, weather, and furious dogs alike.

"The dogs would be easier to handle if you'd lengthen their leashes," suggested Patrick, noticing how one dog was half strangled by its chain.

"You mind your own business, stranger!" shouted the captain. "And be off back to where you came from, for the rascally Irishman you are!"

"I'm not——" began Patrick. Just in time he turned away, realizing it would be dangerous to admit he was not a "rascally Irishman."

He was sorely disappointed, for if the captain would not take him, how could he hope for the freedom he needed for the work he had to do?

With his back to the ship and the sea which he had so much wished to cross, he stood with bent head, and in his heart a prayer—"Open a way for me, O Lord!" With these words he made his supplication. And suddenly he heard a shout, and looking round, saw one of the crew running towards him.

"You are to come with us!" cried the man. "As you seem to be handy with the dogs, the captain will take you, for they are in a savage temper—and I, for one, would be glad to be out of reach of their fangs!"

With a feeling of joy almost too deep for words, Patrick swung round and joined the knot of seamen busy with the ship's gear. The dogs, all bunched together in a snarling mass, were already bundled into the stern. Leaping aboard, Patrick at once went in among them and, with soothing words and gentle touch, soon had them calm and friendly.

"They are grand dogs," was all he said, with a smile.

But the sailors stared at him as if he were a magician. Only the captain looked up from his work at the helm to say, "Well, stranger, if you can manage the waves as well as you have the dogs, you'll be welcome to a passage!"

But Patrick had no such power, and in the wild and dangerous days which followed he was one with the rest upon the ship in hoping that they would not all perish.

At last they came in safely to land upon the coast of Brittany, and there for almost a whole day and night they slept—the dogs, spent and tired, stretched out amongst them. But when they awakened it was to find themselves starving with hunger, and not a thing left upon the anchored ship which they could eat. The waves which had swept over the little vessel had drenched men, dogs, and food with salt water. The dogs were ravenous and grew fierce again.

A sorry band, they went inland hoping to sell some of the dogs, but the poor creatures were so thin and wild that nobody wanted them. Nor were they welcome themselves—they looked so strange and wild, with their long hair, matted beards, and clothes torn to ribbons in the tempest.

"We are like to starve," growled the captain, and crossing over to where Patrick limped on with the others, he shook him by the shoulder saying, "Now, Christian, we have heard a lot about your prayers, but nothing good yet has come of them. This is the time to show us that the God you worship loves all men as you say He does. We are starving. Pray, Christian, pray that food may be sent us."

Then, seeing the plight they were all in, Patrick did as he was asked. His prayer was very simple, and for others more than himself.

And almost at once a herd of wild pigs charged out of the forest, and would have attacked them, but the famished dogs set upon the creatures and killed a great many of them. That night the smell of roast meat made the air sweet to the hungry men, and the dogs slept beside the fire, having eaten as much as they could.

From that time Patrick was looked upon by the captain and his men as one who could work miracles, but he himself claimed no such power. Although he could have lived almost like a king amongst them, he remained in their company for only as long as it was prudent for them all to move in a band. When the dogs had been sold for fair prices, the captain pressed upon Patrick what he said was his fair share of their gains, but Patrick would accept only three pieces of silver. This, he said, would be enough for him until he found some Christian friends who had their home in France. After that, he said, he would take ship to Britain and see if his parents were still alive.

And so he said good-bye to the captain and the sailors with whom he had shared so many hardships, and they parted the best of friends.

But when it came to leaving the few dogs which had not been sold he wept, for they seemed to him the last link with the land he had come to love as if it were his own. Even though he had been a slave there, he could not forget Ireland.

"Some day," he said to himself, "I will go back—carrying the Light of the World with me."

The time came when he did go back, and in a little ship very like the one in which he had escaped from Inver

Dea. He landed with his company of monks who were going to work with him in teaching the Christian Faith—and as we already know, this wonderful man returned as the first Christian Bishop and became St. Patrick, the Patron Saint of Ireland.

LITTLE MIRACLE

LONG, long ago, a child was born in Ireland, who—like the sunshine—had a gift of bringing light into a dark world.

Her father was the Arch-Druid to the High King of Tara, and her mother a Christian lady, daughter of the Chief of Ulster; so she was—in her own right—the equal of any princess in the land.

They called her Bridget, or more often Bride, and it is this last name which she has given, not only to nineteen churches in England, but to many in her native Ireland, and in Scotland as well.

It is said that when she was very young she was taught by St. Patrick, the first Bishop in Ireland. It is quite likely that she was brought up in the Christian faith. And what work she did for it! How notable she became! When quite young she was appointed Abbess of Kildare, and trained under her seven maidens of high birth, who were known as her nuns.

So many stories are told about St. Bridget that it is difficult to choose from them. But perhaps, since Ireland has always been famed for its harp music, the way she used her special powers to fill a silent castle hall with melody will be a good tale to tell.

It seems that the Saint was traveling from one little kingdom to another. With her went her nuns, daughters of kings and princes, of whom there were a great many in the Ireland of that day.

St. Bridget, who was well beloved by all, moved freely about the country among Christian and pagan peoples, and she was never short of a welcome if she knocked on the door of castle or cabin.

And so it came about that, being weary and also rather hungry, she broke her journey at the fort of a Prince of Munster. The Prince and his chief officers—including his harper—were away on some foray. Only his two young sons remained behind. These welcomed St. Bridget and her nuns with the finest hospitality, placing the best they had in the way of food before the unexpected guests, and themselves waiting upon them.

It was the custom in those days for the boys of a royal house to honor guests so. It was also the custom for the harper to play throughout the meal, but on this occasion the harps hung silent on the walls.

St. Bridget, seeing them, called the elder prince to her and said, "Will you and your brother play some of the music of Ireland to us?"

The boy blushed and hung his head, but as the Saint asked him again to follow the custom, he said, "Honored lady, my father and his bard are far away, and the art of playing the harp has not been given either to me or my brother. How gladly we would play and sing to you if we knew how."

St. Bridget smiled, and placing her hand on the boy's head, replied, "Verily I believe you. They say there are even some birds who cannot sing. However, because I feel you have melody within you, I am sure we can call it forth."

The young prince looked up with a smile, and his brother drew nearer to St. Bridget.

"Perhaps, noble lady," he ventured, "if you were to bless our fingers, we might have the power to please you in this."

"Ah, you know me then?" cried St. Bridget, her blue eyes sparkling with pleasure.

"All Ireland knows you," replied the boy.

"Without flattery?" queried St. Bridget with a gay smile, but seeing the boy's puzzlement, she continued, "I mean, are the people of this dear country glad when I move amongst them?"

"Indeed yes," the boy looked at her very seriously. "The

Prince, our father, hopes that you will help him to found a church where our people may be baptized."

"That is the best news I have heard for a long time," said St. Bridget happily. "But now, take down the two harps from the wall. One for each of you, for on this day of days we must rejoice."

The boys went gladly to get the harps. These were small and of great value, having the device of the Prince worked upon the gold of their frames. All the strings were taut and gleaming. St. Bridget looked at them lovingly.

"Ah, the wee fine things," she murmured, "how I treasure a little Irish harp." Then reaching over, she drew a finger across the strings of the one nearest to her, and brought out the most entrancing sound.

"Oh, lady!" cried the elder boy, "please play for us."

But St. Bridget shook her head.

"When I was a child," she said, "I had a harp which the High King of Tara gave to me. He liked to hear me play and sing. But now, I have other things to do. Also, these are your ancestral harps. You must learn to play upon them. Come closer, and from the power Heaven has lent me, I will bless your fingers."

Then, bending her head over the hands of the two boys, she murmured a few words. "And now," she said, "try your skill."

At first the boys were nervous and awkward, but as the

charm of trying grew upon them they did indeed manage to bring out a haunting melody, one which they had heard their old harper play.

And St. Bridget, her blue eyes full of tears because this was a tune she had herself played long ago, forgot that she had said she now had other things to do, and taking one harp into her hands began to play and then to sing. . . .

> How beautiful the day,
> How blue the sky,
> The breeze so soft,
> My heart so glad, that I
> A voice in thanks must raise
> In some sweet song of praise.

And now the nuns who had come with St. Bridget joined in the singing. "Gloria Tibi Domine, Glory to Thee, O Lord," they chanted.

Then, St. Bridget—refreshed and rejoiced—handed the harp back to the elder boy, saying, "Now, try again. Really, if you want to do it, you will find you can."

The boy seized the harp and, having music in him, now played the very music of St. Bridget's song.

"Our lady hath wrought a miracle," said one of the nuns softly.

"Only a very little one then," replied St. Bridget quickly, "and indeed, my sister, I doubt if it was even that. On the fingers of these boys I asked a blessing. The rest came from above."

And so it was always with St. Bridget. The good she did she declared was only lent to her by God. When the first flowers blossomed wherever she passed—the celandines, primroses, cowslips, and other tokens that the long, dark winter is over—she never looked back to see her own trail of glory. But the children who filled their baskets, or made little bunches to carry home, would say to each other, "The dear St. Bridget has passed this way and blessed it." As she blessed the fingers of the little princes so long ago.

THE CLOAK OF ST. BRIDGET

THERE is another story of St. Bridget, that, wanting some land upon which to build a church in Leinster, she went to the King's castle to tell him of her need. But when she got to the gates, the guard told her the King was out hunting and would not be home until sundown.

"Oh, well then," said the Saint, "we will sit down and rest a bit in this nice place, and wait until the King comes home."

And she spread her cloak all about her and spent the time in singing with her nuns.

The day went by, and just as the sun was gilding the top of the castle gates, the sound of the royal hunting-horn was heard. Then, St. Bridget stood up, and the wind, catching her blue cloak, blew it out like a fine flag behind her. And a flag is what the King took it to be when he came in sight of his castle. And it made him angry to see it there.

"Who dares fly any flag but mine over the gates of Leinster?" he cried. "Ride forward, Champion, and find out who the culprit is, then come back here to me."

The Champion galloped off, and soon returned.

"Majesty," he said, "it is not a flag you see but a woman's cloak fluttering in the breeze."

"And what woman dares to flaunt her cloak at my gates?" asked the King, still in a very bad humor.

"It is Bride, Abbess of Kildare, she whom the people call St. Bridget," replied the Champion simply; "and she has come with her nuns because she wishes to ask a gift from Your Majesty."

Now the King knew all about St. Bridget, and the good work she was doing amongst his people. He had heard many tales of her kindness to the poor, the sick, and the sad, and he had willingly given her permission to teach her Faith in Leinster. But learning that she was at his very gates waiting to ask a boon of him, he feared it might be money or something else he did not want to part with, for he was rather a mean man. However, he rode on and gave St. Bridget and her nuns a courtly greeting.

"I saw the blue of your cloak a mile off," he said; "at first I took it for a strange flag."

St. Bridget twitched at her cloak.

"True enough, it's a color that catches the eye," she replied, smiling, and there she stood, tall and straight as a lily and quite as beautiful.

"Now, Bride of Kildare," began the King, "what do you want from me? If it is gold or silver—well, I've neither the one nor the other."

"It's not gold or silver I'm needing," said St. Bridget, and she made a sign to her nuns to stand back, as if she wished to speak in private with the King.

"Well, if it's a dwelling place you're after," went on the King, "I'll tell you straight out that I've neither cot nor cabin to offer you. Many of my own folk sleep under the sky for lack of a better roof."

"With the stars out, there's no better roof than the sky," came the answer; "but it's not a dwelling place I'm asking you for, King of Leinster."

"Now whatever is the girl after?" cried the King, completely puzzled.

Bridget stepped forward and put her white hand on the bridle of his horse. "I see I must tell you what I want," she said, "and little enough it seems to me. All I ask is a wee piece of ground upon which to found a church where your people may worship the highest King of all."

If the King of Leinster didn't quite like the way she put things, he had no fault to find with her Christian

teaching. At the same time he'd no wish to part with any of his land.

"Bride of Kildare," he said, "where would I be getting that piece of ground you're asking for? Isn't it well known that I haven't a spare yard, even to feed a pig on?"

"And isn't it true that I'm only asking you for a bit which wouldn't feed a birdeen, and where nothing—not even thistles—will grow? The barest bit of rock would enchant me," replied St. Bridget.

The King shook his head and would have ridden on, but St. Bridget had a good grip of the bridle.

"Ah now, King," she wheedled, "give in to me, do. Let me have just as much land as my cloak will cover."

The King looked at the Saint and he looked at her cloak, which now she held so neat and tight about her.

"The whole of her and her cloak wouldn't take much room," he thought, "and it's worth a bit of rock to get rid of her."

"I see you'll give me no peace unless I agree," he grumbled, "but mind you, Bride of Kildare, not an inch or an ell this way or that beyond what your cloak will cover."

At that, St. Bridget leapt back from the horse as she let go of the bridle. She let go of her cloak, too, and again the breeze blew it out like a flag behind her.

"Catch hold of my cloak, girls!" she cried, "and away with it!"

There were six of her nuns there, all of them very agile, and each one picked up a bit of the hem of the cloak and they were off, running like hares in different directions.

"Stop, stop!" shouted the astonished King, for it looked as if that blue cloak with St. Bridget in the middle of it would cover the whole of Leinster.

"They won't stop for you," said St. Bridget, when she could speak for laughing. "They can't, you see, because I'm working a little miracle, and they must go on running until it is over."

Yet, in the end, all she would take was just a bit of rocky ground upon which she built a church for the greater good of the King's people.

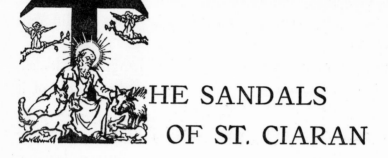

HE SANDALS
OF ST. CIARAN

LONG, long ago—about a hundred years after St. Patrick made his home in Ireland—a holy man from the North, St. Ciaran, left his home to seek peace on Hare Island, which lies in Lough Ree, to the east of Connaught.

As he sat under a tree, wondering of what he should build a hermit's hut, a wild boar crashed through the undergrowth and then fled in terror from the sight of a man, the first he had seen. But, perhaps thinking how tranquil and kind the man had appeared, the boar came back, then retreated again, only to return with enough confidence to snuff at the Saint's hand. And as that hand reached out to stroke and caress the creature's shaggy head, something trusting and kindly sprang up between beast and man so that they became friends.

The boar, using the only way he knew to make himself

useful, severed the branches of trees and rooted up great tussocks of grass, and from these St. Ciaran built his hut. The boar was the Saint's first disciple in that lonely and lovely place; and he served him faithfully and well.

When it became known to other animals that St. Ciaran and the boar had set up house together, a stag, a fox, a badger, a wolf, and a hare came along one by one and, being tamed by the Saint's gentleness, remained also as friends.

Each animal had his duties, and followed the commands of the holy man as if they had been Christian monks. And St. Ciaran, happy with these forest companions, praised God for his goodness in many a prayer and psalm.

But one day, the fox—always the least trusty of the disciples—fell into temptation when he espied St. Ciaran's sandals. These were made of untanned leather, and to the fox smelled as if they might be very good to eat. As it was his turn to guard the hut, he was alone, with no eye to see what he was doing. So, snatching up the sandals in his mouth, he was away like the wind to his lair, which lay deep in the forest.

When St. Ciaran returned—followed by the stag, the wolf, and the badger—he looked first for his sandals and then for the fox who should have been guarding the home. He could see neither. Fox and sandals had disappeared.

"Can it be that Brother Fox has taken my sandals?" he asked. Then he added, "But why should he? What use could he make of them?"

"I can tell you," replied the wolf. "The smell of them reminded him of the days when he was a wild animal, and stole anything he thought would be good to eat."

"Alas," said the stag, "it is very difficult to stop a fox stealing. He has been so used to getting his living that way."

The badger bowed his head and looked mournful. It grieved him to see his master so deceived.

"Perhaps Brother Fox will repent and bring my sandals back," said St. Ciaran; but the animals feared this would not be so.

"It would be best if one of us went after him," suggested the stag, "and I would gladly offer to do so, but then I have no idea how to find his den."

"Nor have I," the wolf told them. "I have always taken good care when I was hunting to keep out of his way. He was so cunning, and so quick on the scent, that he often got the better of me."

"I will go," the badger spoke firmly. "I know the way of the woods, at night especially. Brother Fox will not be able to hide from me. I shall know what to say to him, too, when I find him. I much hope to bring him to repent."

And without more ado the badger rose on his four short legs and went out into the darkness.

"I hope Brother Badger will be all right," said St. Ciaran, rather anxiously. "Brother Fox has very sharp teeth and a very short temper—although he has shown neither to me."

"Do not fear for Brother Badger, dear master," comforted the wolf, "for he is well able to take care of himself. We shall see him return safely, and quite likely with your sandals."

And so they talked of other things while they waited.

In the meantime, the badger had nosed his way through the thickest of the undergrowth and come to a little cave in which the fox had gone to ground. There he sat himself down in the narrow opening and called out severely, "Brother Fox, Brother Fox! Are you not ashamed of yourself for playing such a mean trick upon our good master? Did he not trust you to guard his property? But what did you do but steal it! Fie upon you, out upon you, bad servant and false friend!"

Then the fox, who had just begun to gnaw one of the sandals, dropped it, and crouched quaking inside his den. He had good reason to fear the badger, who was more than his match unless he, himself, was on the run.

"What a fuss you make about a little thing, Brother Badger," he replied boldly. "True, I borrowed the master's sandals, but I was going to bring them back again very soon."

"You have rewarded good with evil," said the badger

45

sternly, "but there is still time to make amends. If you have not already devoured the sandals, bring them out, and come back to the hermitage with me."

"I shall come when it pleases me . . ." began the fox, with a great show of courage, but the badger interrupted him angrily.

"Come out when I tell you, or I'll come in and bite off your ears, pull out your brush and tweak your whiskers!" he threatened.

And the fox knew the badger well enough to be sure he would carry out his threat. So he picked up the sandals again between his teeth, and trotted out with them into the moonlight.

"See, here they are!" he said brightly, "and none the worse. And what do we do now?"

"You follow me, with your tail between your legs, until we get back to the hermitage," growled the badger.

And the fox went meekly home.

When St. Ciaran took the sandals into his hands and saw they were quite unharmed, he said sadly, "Brother Fox, Brother Fox! How could you do this to me? Have I not trusted and loved you, made you one of my disciples and given you a home? Have I not shared with you all I had? Yet you carried off two old bits of leather—which might have choked you in the end."

At this the fox hung his head and promised, in his own

46

way, never more to offend his good master. And to show his full repentance he refused all food until the saint commanded him to break his fast.

Then the other animals also forgave him, and he became one of their happy band again.

It is said that this was the foundation of a famous monastery where many Christian men came to sit at the feet of the good St. Ciaran. But of all those who remained as his disciples, he loved none better than his faithful forest friends.

 A BRIDE FROM THE SEA

Malcolm Canmore, King of Scotland, sat in a turret room of his castle at Dunfermline. It was a gloomy enough place with its rough stone walls misted over with spiders' webs, and only wooden benches in place of chairs. The King saw nothing amiss with it, nor that no sunlight came in through the narrow slits in the thick walls. These were meant only for the use of an archer to pick off an enemy below.

All the same, King Malcolm felt both weary and dejected. He had that feeling which comes to most men who are almost always at war. He had other reasons, too, for his low spirits. His wife had long since died, and there was no mistress of the castle to look after things. Servants in plenty there were, but they were always quarreling. He could hear them now—down in the courtyard below

49

—shouting at each other, disputing angrily over some trifle while the children fought with the dogs for a bone or scrap of food. For the times were very rough, and nowhere rougher than in Scotland and the North of England of that time.

As the noise grew worse, so did the King's temper. He was tired of the strife and muddle amid which he lived. Something within himself told him there must be a better way even for a fighting king to spend his life.

"I must get me a wife," he thought, glancing down at the torn edges of his plaid which no woman had brought a needle and thread to mend. Yes, he must marry again —but whom?

He went over in his mind all the daughters of his earls. Not one of them would do. And so he began to make a picture in his mind of the woman he would invite to be his queen.

"She must be tall and slender," he decided, "with blue eyes and golden hair—and a soft way of speaking, for I do hate a lass to scream at me. And when she moves, her silken robes should make a gentle swish like the wind rustling in the long grass——"

A sudden thought struck him that this picture was only of the lady's outside, and he began another. "And she must have a sweet temper—since mine is so hot—and bear with me when I am angry. She must be fond of children and not afraid of big dogs. I would wish her, I think, to be a Christian although I am such a pagan." He sighed. "And I won't find her in my own kingdom," his thought ran on, as he got up from the hard bench upon which he had been sitting and put an eye to the arrow-slit.

Beneath him he could see the Firth of Forth sparkling in the sunlight, and beyond, the tumbling raging waters of the North Sea. For it had been a wild night, and he hoped the fishermen had pulled up their boats to safety. If not, many of them would have been lost.

At this thought, others as gloomy skipped about like black imps in his mind.

"Who'd be a king?" he cried aloud. "I'd far rather be a shepherd lad herding sheep on yonder hills—or a fisher-boy down by the water's edge!"

Had he been either, then he might have been the first to see a little ship which, nearly disabled, its sails torn to ribbons, crept in like a wounded dog, for shelter from the gale.

A crowd watching on the beach saw the ship's slow progress, and when it seemed as if it would never make an anchorage a dozen fishermen ran to their boats, and hauling them down the shingle, launched them smartly and pulled out to offer aid. For men of the sea have their own loyalties, and no matter from where a ship comes, if it is in distress away go the boats from shore to the rescue.

And while the fishermen made haste with loud hails of encouragement, the women watched and wondered if there was any woman or child on board. If so—and they consulted with each other—a shawl here and a skirt there must be spared and offered to anyone in need.

There was a woman on board—although no child. But what a woman! She is still remembered in songs and tales. She had, they say, the beauty of an angel and the grace of a golden lily. When she spoke her voice held the music of little harps.

So, when they saved her from the almost sinking ship, and when the women had cared for her and comforted her, they took her to their king. "For," said they, "this is a lady of high degree." But why such a one was in such a plight they did not know.

King Malcolm Canmore came out himself to greet the lady, and to offer the best that his castle could afford. But as he looked at her—pale after her ordeal, but calm and steadfast as she stood in his great hall—he remembered the picture he had made in his own mind of the wife he desired, and exulted to himself, "She has come, she has come! My bride from the sea!"

But aloud, he said gently, "Tell me, lady, your name, and what rough wind—save that of weather—has brought you here."

"My name is Margaret," she replied; "and I am the sister of the Child Atheling, who by right should sit upon England's throne."

King Malcolm's hand sought the dirk at his side. "And, by heaven, if might is right—so he shall!" he cried. Then, seeing her shrink from his violence, he tried to make his voice as soft as the coo of a dove. "But you are weary, lady, and need rest. The best my castle and my kingdom contain I offer you." And then he added in rather a shame-faced way, "I fear it is very bleak and rough here. You see, I have no wife to make it any better."

The lady smiled, and it was as if the sun had come out in that gloomy hall. "I shall do very well," she said, "and be ever grateful to you, my lord, for the refuge from our enemies you give me. I don't know where else I could go."

"All Scotland is yours," declared King Malcolm.

His earls stared! Was this their stern leader, the fearless fighter, and victor in a score of border battles, now speaking so softly, so gently to the lady from the sea?

That day, every man and woman for a mile around had to bestir themselves to help fit out the Castle rooms which were being prepared for the English princess. And while they worked they talked of her beauty, her sweetness, and the way the King watched her as she moved about the great, gaunt hall. He had built up a couch beside the hearth and piled it with furs. And here, while she rested, her hand on the neck of one of his great dogs, she told him the story of her escape.

Until William of Normandy had won at the Battle of Hastings she had been in a convent in Northumberland, but because of her rank and also being sister to the Saxon Atheling, it had been thought unwise to let her stay in England. And so, a stout ship had been fitted out with such comfort as the times allowed, and in the dead of night it had put out to sea.

"But then we met with your North Sea weather, my lord," she said smilingly, as he looked down upon her from his great height.

"What a ruffian he looks," she thought, "but I don't think he is really. If his hair were combed and that great beard trimmed, he might even appear a handsome man."

And King Malcolm was thinking, as she settled her veil over her golden hair, "What can I do to win her?"

It took time for him to do so. Many moments there were when she shrank from his rough voice and violent ways. Although courteous and gentle to her, she watched him with his servants and saw that to him a little child meant scarcely more than a dog. She saw, too, that he was restless and unhappy—unless he was sitting beside her and taking in every word she said.

But when the day came that he asked her to be his

wife, she thought most of the fact that she was a Christian, and that he—so far—knew nothing about her faith at all. If he prayed to any god it was the god of war. And she was of royal parentage also. She had been brought up at the court of her uncle, Edward the Confessor, king and saint, who had built the first Abbey of Westminster.

She still wanted to be a nun, but here was a lonely king, growing a little old, powerful—but neglected. She felt that there was work for her to do here. Not only to turn this great, gloomy castle into a place of sweetness and light, but also to turn this great and gloomy king into a servant of Christ. And this she longed most eanestly to do.

"Give me a little time in which to make up my mind," she said very gently.

"Not too long," he urged. "You see, in your company my heart is growing lighter every day. Besides, the people need you."

That moved her. There was indeed so much to do amongst the women and children, among the poor, the sick, and the old. She had thought of life in a convent as being nearer to Heaven than any other place on earth. Now she began to feel that she could do God's work just as well in this dark castle. "Only it shall not remain dark. I will work and work to bring in the sunlight."

And so Princess Margaret of England was married to

the King of Scotland, with all the pomp that was possible in those far-away days. No bells rang, for there were no churches. No boys' sweet voices sang their wedding music. But the Princess Margaret's own priest proclaimed them man and wife, and for the first time King Malcolm bent the knee at a Christian service.

Directly she was made a queen, this lovely Margaret began her work of making a happier world for her husband's people. From the first they were devoted to her and did her will. It is said that she taught the women first to sew and then to embroider—after which, she employed many of them in working on tapestries to hang on the ugly stone walls of the castle hall.

Where hard benches had been made to serve even as seats for royalty, she found craftsmen in wood to make chairs. Where even royal heads had slept on bundles of skins, there were now plump pillows stuffed with feathers. And most wonderful of all, at royal banquets the guests were served off dishes of silver and gold.

Just where the young Queen found all these things, or how she got them safely into the castle, has never been really told. But for centuries afterwards they could be seen, and so we must believe she had them.

A certain splendor was, to her, the right of kings and queens—just as it was the right of their subjects to gain an honest living. She wished every man employed, and every woman in a home of her own. And for little children she had so great a love that there was always a group round her knee. Not the children of her husband's nobles, but those without parents—forlorn and without either love or care.

Sometimes King Malcolm would find her feeding them out of a silver bowl with a golden spoon. And then he would ask her if wooden bowls and spoons were not more suitable.

"We have everything of the best, husband," she would say, "but these little ones have never known anything but the worst. I would give them all some small joy to remember."

And so, this English princess, this bride from the sea, changed not only the rough hard soldier—her husband—into a kind and Christian man, but his whole kingdom. During her reign, churches were built and hospitals. The hungry were fed, the sick tended, and life became for all a better and a happier thing.

Little wonder is it that Queen Margaret was sainted. Little wonder is it that when she had left this earth her memory remained as fresh and sweet as her own heart had ever been—or that the poor and orphaned children long, long afterwards would say or sing:

> St. Margaret of Scotland,
> She had the gowden hair,
> St. Margaret of Scotland,

She had the bonny air.
And oh to be in Scotland
When St. Margaret was there!

St. Margaret of Scotland,
Was good as she was fair,
St. Margaret of Scotland,
Upheld the orphans' prayer,
And oh to be in Scotland
When St. Margaret was there!

THE WOLF OF GUBBIO

In the days when St. Francis of Assisi taught the love of everything which God had made, and himself treated all men as brothers, he paid a visit to the little town of Gubbio, which is perched on a hillside and looks much the same today as it did in the Saint's time.

It was growing dark when he arrived there, but all the same, he was much surprised to find the streets deserted. Not a light showed, not a mule bell tinkled, and no friendly voices called out to him, "Welcome, Brother Francis, welcome! It is good to have you back again."

"Strange," thought St. Francis; "before, even the children have come running headlong to meet me."

Then a light patch on a dark tree trunk caught his eye. Going closer to the tree, the Saint made out the warning written there: "Beware of the Wolf!" it read.

"Ha," murmured St. Francis, "so that is what has frightened the good folk of Gubbio, and sent them into hiding behind closed doors. 'Beware of the Wolf!' I expect, Brother Wolf, you have been up to some of your ugly tricks again. We must look into this."

Now St. Francis not only had great power over men, but also over animals. Even the birds showed no fear of him. They would perch upon his shoulder, or hop about his feet, and he would say, "Little Sister Sparrow!" or "Brother Raven!" whichever feathered friend came his way.

But a wolf—and such a one as the Wolf of Gubbio— was it really possible for anyone to treat such a fierce creature like a brother? Well, St. Francis thought so. And as he knocked on the door of a friend with his staff, he smiled to himself as a rather timid voice called out, "Who's there?"

"Francis of Assisi," came the quick reply, upon which a chain was let down and the door opened just wide enough to allow the visitor through.

"I thought you were expecting me," said the Saint, looking all round at a group of frightened people.

An old crone hobbled up to him, peering at his face with dim eyes.

"Oh, how glad we are you have come safely past the peril of the woods," she quavered, "for only last week my daughter's cousin was attacked by that villain of a wolf, and only saved herself by flinging him her best fowl."

"Well, I had no fowl to fling," said St. Francis, "but I neither saw nor heard the wolf. I am sorry he has been so troublesome."

"Troublesome!" echoed a man, shaking his fist as if at the wolf. "That's a kind word for him! He's the terror of the whole countryside. From here to the next village no one dare venture out after sunset. And we have to barricade ourselves in, or he'd smell us out!"

"I've a terror of his coming down the chimney," put in a young woman who held a baby in her arms. "For days I've not dared to take my baby out, in case the brute was bold enough to leap on us and snatch the child from under my shawl."

"Dear me!" said St. Francis. "Things are worse than they should be in Gubbio. What is the next thing to be done?"

"We shall have to make up a party, armed with spears and hatchets," said a young man, "and somehow hound the wolf to his death."

"Oh, no!" cried St. Francis, "after all, he does not know he is doing wrong. He is most likely half-starving, old, and short of teeth. He'd be with the pack if they'd have him. Lone wolves are almost always nearing the end of their days."

"His days have been far too many for the folk of Gubbio," retorted an old man, half angrily. "Don't make ex-
cuses for him, Fra Francesco. We've got to rid the place
of him, or no one will be safe. Think of the children!
Why, they daren't go out to play for fear he'll spring out
at them."

St. Francis sighed. It always made him sad to find
creatures at war with each other, hating each other, destroying each other.

"I'll tell you what I will do," he said suddenly. "This
wolf now, where does he hide?"

Half a dozen voices answered him, "Where the road to
Assisi enters the forest."

"I know," nodded St. Francis. "It is dark under the
trees there, even at noon. I'll go that way tomorrow and
wait for Brother Wolf, and see what he has to say for
himself."

Many cried out at this. It was risking a terrible death!
The wolf was of enormous size—and as to being a brother!
He was a cruel enemy to all mankind!

St. Francis listened quietly. Then raised a gentle hand.

"Listen," he began, "there is no creature that God has
made who is quite without feeling. Leave the wolf to me.
I will see if I can tame his wild heart."

There was a muttering and a murmuring, but St.
Francis began to talk of other things and soon everyone

was cheered and hopeful, while the children gathered about his knees and asked him to tell them more about his friends the birds.

The next day, an hour or two before sunset, St. Francis set out alone on the road which led to the forest, it being his intention to wait for the Wolf of Gubbio at that point where the creature was wont to spring upon his prey. In vain the men implored him to arm himself with both hatchet and spear, but this the Saint would not do, saying, "All I will carry is my staff. But be of good cheer! The wolf will not harm me."

The children clung to his robe to detain him, and some of the women wept.

"If it is for us you go out to almost certain death," cried one, "then, blessed Brother Francis, we will not accept the sacrifice."

All the same, the Saint remained firm in his purpose and left the town alone.

It was nearing the end of a day early in winter, and the mountains were already capped with snow. Below, the plains still basked in sunshine, and the sound of bells tinkled merrily as the mules came up the steep and stony paths from the valley. Soon they would be safely tethered in. So deep was the fear of the great wolf in both man and beast that neither would be seen outside when dusk fell.

But St. Francis was not thinking of the wolf at all, but of the many wonders God had made—the Sun, the Moon, the myriad Stars, the Wind, and the gracious Rain. To him all these were as brothers and sisters, and of them he sang as he went along.

> Be thou praised, my Lord, with all thy creatures,
>> Above all Brother Sun,
> Who gives the day and light to us,
>> And is beautiful and radiant.
> Be thou praised, my Lord, of Sister Moon and the stars.
> Be thou praised of Brother Wind and Sister Rain,
>> And of our Sister Mother Earth, who gives us
>> Luscious fruits and lovely flowers. . . .

And so, singing, and too happy to feel fear, St. Francis came to the spot where the road entered the dark forest, and there he sat down on a flat stone and waited for the wolf.

The sun went down, and almost at once the moon rose, bathing the figure of the Saint in silvery light. Rising to stretch himself, his shadow fell across the opening to the forest—appearing twice as tall as he was himself. It was almost as if a giant kept him company. He spread out his arms. The shadow did the same. And then he slowly brought his arms round until his two hands were folded on his breast.

As shadows will, his copied every movement. And there between Saint and shadow-giant sprang the Wolf of Gubbio. But here was something that no wolf had ever seen

—a man, and one who was not a man and terrible! The wolf shrank back with a whine.

Then St. Francis, seeing the wolf retreat, called to him, saying, "Brother Wolf, be not afraid of a shadow, nor of me. I do not come to destroy you but to reason with you. For many of your days you have worked much evil, by destroying God's creatures and offending against His Holy Laws. All the same, Brother Wolf, I have come to make peace with you. If you promise to mend your ways I will forgive and protect you. The men of Gubbio have sworn to be avenged for the harm you have done. They plan to hunt you with hatchets, spears, and dogs, for they are angry—and with just cause."

All this St. Francis said in so firm and yet so gentle a voice that the wolf in some way seemed to understand that this fearless human being had not come to hurt him. And it is said that the wild creature—so savage and so hated by men—advanced towards the Saint, and bowed his shaggy head in reverence.

Smiling, St. Francis continued, "I see that at heart you are a gentle wolf, and only hunger and loneliness have led you into villainy. Come, follow me. I promise you that if you do no harm you shall not be harmed. Also, you shall never go hungry, nor be hunted by men with dogs and spears. I will give you such a good character to the people of Gubbio that from this day you shall have

nothing to fear from them."

The night went by. It was cold under the starlit sky, but the heart of the Saint was warm within him when he remembered the strange new convert to gentleness he had made. How often he had told his brethren that "perfect love casteth out fear," and here, almost as if on guard, the wolf lay at his feet.

The sun rose and it was time to go home. But to the wild animal tamed by human kindness, home could only be where his new friend was. And so he followed him, humbly, faithfully as any dog. In this way St. Francis returned, unhurt and full of rejoicing, with the wolf loping obediently at his heels.

The grateful creature remained at Gubbio—fed by the women and petted by the children—until he died.

Then said St. Francis, "It was as I told you. This was a lone wolf, exiled from the pack because he was too old to hunt."

And the children brought little bunches of flowers which they had picked themselves, and wept to show their love for this dumb friend, for they grieved that they would see him no more going tamely about among them.

HE

GRATEFUL DUCK

THE wild ducks were ready to fly—as the time had come for them to seek a better feeding-ground. For weeks, the parent birds had been training the young ones to follow them to the water's edge by marching at the head of their family and calling out "Dreek dreek," the cry of their clan. And all the ducklings had done pretty well—all except the youngest. No matter how his mother pecked him; no matter how she quacked at him; it was no use. Just as soon as they were all ready to plunge into the sea, then he stopped dead, cheeping mournfully.

And as to using his wings! Although sometimes he would just manage to rise a foot or two in the air, he always came down with a flop on the wet sand, or rock, uttering cries of shame and terror.

But one day—long after his brothers had learned to fly

round and round in beautiful formation—he did take a clumsy fall into a shallow pool, and found himself swimming for dear life, and not at all because he was enjoying it.

However, his mother now thought well enough of him to make the winter move, and although this meant flying over a short stretch of rocky foreshore, she thought he could just about do it and come safely to the creek beyond. But as he was still clumsy on the wing, she decided to fly behind him, letting the father bird lead the others. And very handsome the parent bird looked in his clean white collar, the wide, steel-blue bars of his wings bordered with white, as he led his squadron in perfect formation out to sea.

But it was at this proud moment that the youngest duckling managed to disgrace himself yet once again, for although he rose clumsily on his new wings, no sooner did he find himself borne up into the sky than his heart failed him and he came hurtling down upon the rocks beneath. As ill luck would have it, he fell into a deep cleft where he stuck, wedged so tightly that he could hardly cheep.

Quite unprepared for this calamity, his mother dropped in her flight and peered with her beady eye down at her captive child. Although the cleft was not deep, it was quite out of her power to rescue him. All she could do was to stare down at him in an agony of fear.

It was then, like a ray of hope, that the memory of a kind human friend came to her: the hermit—St. Bartholomew, saint and servant of God—who lived in a rock cave a little way up on the cliff.

On one of his walks along the seashore, he had come upon her nest and, fearful of disturbing her, had slipped off his sandals and moved away on bare feet.

As the spring was a hard and cold one, something prompted him to place a small portion of his scanty corn near enough for her to find it. He also brought her daily a shallow pannikin of water from the spring where he drew his own.

And when the ducklings—eight of them—were all hatched out, he came every morning to watch them, when, like little balls of yellow down, they clambered over their proud mother, cheeping and peeping like a chorus of crickets.

The Saint took great pleasure in watching their merry antics, while they, seeing him so often, lost all fear and rushed to meet him, at once pecking at the hem of his cassock or plucking the cord hanging loosely from his waist; and always ready with open beaks to be fed.

He grew quite fond of this wild duck family, and the mother soon treated him as an old and honored friend. She would walk all around him, followed by the young ones, then cock her head on one side and give a gratified quack, as if to say: "They are rather nice, aren't they?"

And so, the Saint felt a pang when he realized that they intended to fly, for one morning he went out very early, and there they all were, so near to the sea that one movement forward would plunge them into it.

Somehow, the Saint felt that this was not a good moment in which to say good-bye, and so he turned and went back to his prayers, feeling more lonely than he had ever felt before.

So he did not see the little accident, nor know the difficulty in which his feathered friend was placed.

And she, helpless to rescue the duckling, thought, "Does he really not know up there what is happening to us here, down below? When we were hungry he brought us food. When we were thirsty he saw that we had fresh water."

Confident in the power of the Saint to help her, she went to fetch him, followed by the sound of her child's piteous cries.

To save time she flew, for she was a slow waddler. And as she alighted with a harsh whirr of wings St. Bartholomew looked up from his book of devotions and could not believe his eyes. Was it indeed his friend the wild duck, who surely must have flown only a little while ago with all her family? But she, with no time to waste, pattered up to him, a whole world of entreaty in her eyes. Then, finding that he did not at once guess her dire need of him, she opened her beak and clapped it down on his right hand, and, as a child does when it wants to show anyone some strange sight at a distance, she began to drag at the Saint as if to get him up from his knees.

"What can you want with me?" he cried, when the duck let go of his hand to seize the hem of his cassock. He rose from the floor, and at once it was plain she was really trying to pull him out of the cave.

"I see I must go with you," said St. Bartholomew, "even if it is into the sea!"

And he followed the duck down the cliff path, she still holding on to his robe. The distance to the water was not great, for the tide was coming in. The rock where the duckling had fallen would very soon be covered by the sea.

"I wonder," thought the Saint, "if this poor creature has some vital purpose in hauling me along? But if we go much farther, it seems likely I may be drowned. At any rate, I shall have to wade out to the rock, and what then?"

But still the duck held on to him, and when she reached the sea plunged in, swimming strongly towards the rock, where she knew her little one might soon perish.

As the sea was shallow, the Saint waded out, and clambering up the slimy, slippery rock heard the faint "cheep cheep" he knew so well. Looking down, he saw the duckling heaving and struggling in its desperate attempts to get free.

"Now rest easy, good Mother Duck," comforted the Saint, "for surely you have not led me here to fail in the rescue of your Benjamin."

And who knows at what risk to himself the Saint knelt on the rock, or with what skill and tenderness he released the baby duck from its cruel trap and brought it safely to its mother's side?

With a peck she set it upon its webbed feet, then, to the Saint's surprise, rose on her wings and let out a quack of scorn, as if to say, "Follow me if you like. If not, drown where you are!"

For an instant the duckling gaped with open beak at its soaring mother. Then, with some dim understanding that the time had come to make a proper effort, expanded its wings and took off—not without courage.

At first its flight was uncertain, but at every yard gained in steadiness, and when finally overtaking its mother, the duckling cried out, "Dreek dreek," as if to ask her if she could manage.

Then, and only then, the Mother Duck swung round, and followed by her wondering duckling, caught up St. Bartholomew just as he had waded to the shore. Alighting almost at his bare feet, she dipped her head in a

humble reverence. The duckling did the same.

"Ah, that was nice of you, little Sister Duck!" exclaimed the Saint joyfully. For he quite understood that she had returned to thank him for the rescue of her duckling, and to show that she was grateful.

A BASKET
OF ROSES

IT is not every child who can be born to a silver cradle. But hundreds of years ago a little princess was not only rocked to sleep in one, but also took her first journey over high mountains and through dark forests, wrapped in soft furs and traveling in a silver cradle as if it were a litter.

She was Princess Elizabeth of Hungary, and she started on this great adventure when she was just four years old.

In those days it was usual for the sons and daughters of a royal house to be betrothed when they were still quite tiny children. Directly matters were settled, the little royal lady would be packed off to her future home, there to be brought up by the bridegroom's mother in the ways of his family.

So Elizabeth traveled from Hungary to Germany, and

when she was fourteen she was married to the Grand Duke Ludwig of Thuringia. And as the young people really loved each other, their happiness was deep and true. Now and again the young wife found her husband's mother, the old Duchess, rather difficult to get on with, but when, in course of time, three children—a son and two daughters—were born to the young couple, their cup of joy was full.

In the midst of her busy and important life, the young Duchess never forgot the sick, the poor, and the sorrowful, so many of whom came to the Castle gates to beg for alms. With her own hands she would feed them, and with those same hands bind up their wounds or bathe their sores.

For the little children she had a special tenderness, and it was said she would take garments intended for her own son and daughters and dress some ragged waif in the fine clothes herself.

When these stories came to the ears of the old Duchess she was much annoyed. Sending for her son, she said to him, "Listen! This is what your wife has done now. Given a cloak of scarlet cloth to a charcoal-burner's child! And I am told, too, that as fast as the cooks bake fine white bread for our table she piles up as much as a big basket will hold, and carries it herself to the gates!"

The young Duke, who loved his wife so dearly, fired up

and replied, "To me, everything Elizabeth does is right. If she feels we have too much, and others too little, why should she not show her charity?"

"I have always been charitable to the poor myself," retorted the old Duchess, "but never have I been known to stand amongst the beggars outside the Castle gate, or bare my head in church as Elizabeth did when a child. You will do well to mention these things to her, my son, and tell her there is much talk about her odd behavior. Born a princess she may be. A royal duchess she now is. But that does not excuse her running in and out like any poultry maid."

"Oh come, come!" cried the young Duke. "Elizabeth is a pattern of all a lady of rank should be."

"Well, I don't know about that," replied his mother. "And a good wife—whatever her rank—should not squander her husband's goods. White bread is not for beggars. Black bread is best for them, and at least seven days old."

Now Duke Ludwig, although he resented his mother's remarks about Elizabeth, did feel that his wife carried her charity a little too far. Only that morning he had come upon her feeding some little orphan children in her own beautiful room. With a sickly baby on her lap she was coaxing it to take some milk out of a golden spoon.

"Just look, Ludwig!" she said, her eyes shining with

pity, "the little creature is lapping up the milk quite well."

"Don't let it swallow the gold spoon," Ludwig returned unsmilingly. And so when his mother took up the tale of Elizabeth's wide charities, in his heart he felt she went too far.

But at this time he said nothing. He could not bear to scold her, she was so sweet and so anxious to please.

So every day Elizabeth carried her gifts to the Castle gates, where her coming brought more joy and light than even the sunrise.

And as the crowd of beggars grew, so did the size of her gifts. Where she had bestowed six loaves, now twelve were not enough. To no one else would she hand over the task of carrying the basket, piled up with new bread and always covered with a fine white cloth. Directly her first prayers were said, she sped away to the bakery, saw the basket filled with warm white loaves—and although often hungry herself, would not pause to break her own fast until the waiting people were fed.

Then how gratefully they blessed her, and how their thanks sounded as music in her ears! She would run home singing, and play with her own children as if she were again a child herself.

But one day the Master Baker complained to the Grand Duke's Steward that the young Duchess daily took off enough fresh bread for a banquet. And the Steward told the Grand Duke.

"Ha!" thought the Duke, "I'll find out for myself the truth of these tiresome stories. I shall go out betimes and catch my pretty breadstealer, and tell her this sort of thing can't go on."

So one morning the Grand Duke got up much earlier than usual—only to find that Elizabeth was earlier still. He went to the window, and there she was, standing amongst the roses, a great basket on her arm. Then she began to move slowly away, as if thinking earnestly of something.

"Oh, Elizabeth," mourned the Duke to himself, "I hate to spy upon you, but this time I must stop you carrying that basket to the Castle gates."

Then, running downstairs, he let himself out by a side door, knowing that if he was quick enough he would be the other side of the rosary before his wife could get there. And so he met her face to face.

She smiled at him radiantly. "Oh, Ludwig!" she cried in delight; "you are up early! Isn't it delicious out here among the roses?"

"Why, yes—and you look like a rose yourself," he replied. "But let me carry your basket. What is there in it?"

She looked at him. Her smiled faded. With trembling lips she tried to speak . . . but no words came, and she seemed as if about to cry. And there the two of them stood in silence—those two young people who loved one another so dearly—the basket between them.

"What is in the basket?" asked the Duke again, and this time his voice was rough and troubled.

Still Elizabeth did not answer, but from her heart she prayed—"Please, God, make Ludwig trust me!" and suddenly her face brightened. Her voice came back to her.

"My basket?" she said gaily. "You may peep into it if you wish." And she twitched the linen cloth aside, and there were only roses—red and white roses.

"Forgive me, Elizabeth," said her husband. "How could I ever have doubted you, or have thought for one moment that you could ever be untrue? From this day you shall bestow your blessings where and how you will —for I think that today we have shared a miracle."

"A miracle!" she repeated in a rapt tone. "Oh, Ludwig, I think that too. For just now when you seemed to doubt me, I asked God to put it into your heart to trust me. And you do trust me, don't you?"

"Indeed I do," he replied, "I both trust and revere you, my little Saint."

For the rest of her life Elizabeth continued in her good works. Many sorrows she had, but she put them aside to soothe the sorrows of others. And whenever it was hers to choose between two crowns, the one of gold and the

other of thorns, she was never in any doubt—remembering that the King of the World and of Heaven had also chosen a Crown of Thorns.

ST. ROQUE
AND HIS DOG

In an old book called *The Golden Legend* there is a story of a man and his dog—the dog so wise and faithful that when his master was near to death it was the dog who saved his life.

It happened like this.

About six hundred years ago the plague—which was sometimes called "The Black Death"—swept over Europe and was at its worst in Northern Italy. So many people died that even in cities few of the living were seen. All those who could, fled from the scourge to the mountains, the forest, and all open spaces. The roads were crowded not only with people but also with carts, caravans, animals, and every kind of traffic. And the dust these refugees made hung on the sultry air like low thunder clouds.

At night the wolves—never far away—hunted in packs

through deserted streets where the houses looked like ruins, for most of them had the roofs torn off so that rats and mice could not harbor there and spread the disease.

To a young pilgrim arriving in Piacenza from France when the plague was at its height the place seemed almost a city of the dead.

His name was Roque, and he was of a noble family of Montpellier, then a great port of call, through which ran the highway to Spain.

What had brought him so far from home? He was young, he was handsome, and rich enough to enjoy life's pleasures. Yet here he was, in a pilgrim's robe and carrying a pilgrim's staff, in the almost deserted Piacenza, with a little brown dog at his heels.

An old priest carrying a lantern peered at the young stranger. He himself was not at all afraid of plague. He had had it, and was not likely to get it again. And so he had not run off with the others, but remained to help the sick and comfort the bereaved. His cassock was tattered and his face was thin and drawn, for famine so often follows pestilence, and even water was very scarce in Piacenza. The shops were closed and the market empty. It was a scene of desolation indeed.

"Who are you, and why do you come here?" asked the priest.

"My name is Roque," replied the pilgrim, "and I come to be of what help I can."

"Are you a doctor?" the priest continued.

"No," replied Roque, "although I know a little about healing the sick."

"But who can have told you of our troubles?" wondered the priest.

"Bad news travels fast, and, besides, I have met many fugitives on the road," said Roque; "all told me the same dread story."

"It won't help them much to run away," put in the priest grimly. "They will not escape that way. Every part of the country is in the grip of this evil. How is it with you in France?"

"In the South from where I come, we were still healthy," replied Roque, "and it seemed to me that one might be some help here, if one came."

"It was a good wish," commended the priest. "We have no doctors and hardly any medicines. Bread and water are scarce, and the children cry out for food. A few brave men and women have remained, and we still have one baker—I pray he may not take the disease."

"Is there anywhere I could sleep tonight?" asked Roque.

"Well, if you do not mind its being under the stars, there is my house," offered the priest. "You see, we have stripped all our roofs off, believing that rats and mice carry the infection."

"The stars will do well for me," said Roque, smiling. "I have some bread and meat in my pack. I shall be glad if you will share it with me."

"Come along then," and the priest held up his lantern to show the way. "Later on we shall have the wolves, and so your dog had best be behind closed doors."

"He's not my dog really," said Roque. "I looked round just as I entered the town and found him sniffing at my heels. I shooed him off, but he looked so unhappy that I gave him a pat, and this he took as permission to follow me. I suppose he is lost or was left behind when his master decamped."

"Very likely," agreed the priest. "There are hundreds of dogs and cats left here to starve, and as to donkeys! You could acquire a dozen for nothing, for no one will now claim them."

The dog—who appeared to have been listening to the conversation—now began to run round in circles, then made little excursions forward to show the way. But after almost every movement he returned to sidle up against Roque's robe, as if to say, "I may go ahead a little, but I shall always come to heel when my master bids me."

And so the three went up the deserted street until the priest stopped in front of a narrow, dark house, which was, as he had said, quite roofless. And this was to be Roque's home for many a day, until one came when the priest went out and did not return. No one could say what had happened to him, and Roque felt very unhappy, for he had become fond of the old man. Now he was quite alone with the dog who had adopted him, and whom he had named Tino, that being as good a name as any other.

Through all the weeks in which Roque had lived with the old priest in Piacenza, he had found much work to do. Every morning the pair of them had set out to visit the sick and to feed the children. This last was not always easy, for the baker was running short of flour, and one small loaf was often all he could make for them. It was Roque who fetched the bread, and with him went the dog Tino.

But one day Roque could not go. He was watching over a sick child who wept and clung to him if he so much as moved from the bedside. And there also was Tino, sitting on his haunches and staring at his master, doing everything a dog could to show sympathy and understanding.

And suddenly Roque thought, "I believe Tino could get the bread!" And Tino beat his stumpy tail on the mud floor, as if to say, "Of course Tino could," and then sprang up to show he was ready.

Roque looked about for something which he could fasten round Tino's neck in which the bread might travel safely. Ah, there was the very thing! A rough, round basket with a lid. And to the handle of this he tied a label on which he wrote: "Please send bread back with my dog."

And oh how delighted Tino was to be made so important! He had almost all his legs off the ground at once with glee. Then he whined to be let out because, clever as he was, he could not reach the latch to lift it.

"And away you go," said Roque, laughing for the first time in many weeks, as Tino bounded off, the basket swinging round his neck. "What a useful fellow," thought his master, and suddenly realized how much he had come to love the dog, and how grim life would be without him.

Tino brought the loaf back quite safely and with great pride in his feat. After this he went to the baker daily, and although the flour was so low in the bin, there was always bread in Tino's basket.

This was a source of joy to Roque, for it meant that some hungry child could have a slice. He would have been almost happy had it not been for his anxiety about his old friend the priest.

"Perhaps," thought Roque, "he has had an accident, or been taken ill in some lonely spot."

He began to think he must go in search of the missing man. So, leaving Tino to guard the house, he set off early one morning to look. As he left, the dog began to whine and howl, beating his paws upon the closed door. He tore round and round trying to find some way of escape, some way of following his master. But it was of no use. And so he just sat down and began to howl most miserably again.

"Poor fellow," thought Roque, "but if I'm late, the wolves might easily snatch him." And he went on his way.

As he passed through the narrow streets, his fair head bare to the sun, some who saw him said, "Ah, that one, he is a saint—if not an angel from heaven. St. Roque we will call him, for a halo would well become him."

But of all he asked, Roque could glean no tidings of the old priest. And as the sun set and the sky began to darken he turned to go home. Tino would be waiting for him. Tino would be quite distracted by his long absence.

"I am very tired," thought Roque, leaning heavily upon his staff, "and I don't see as well as I should, but perhaps that is because my head aches from being so long in the sun."

It was hours since he had eaten; hours since he had unwound the sick child's arms from around his neck; hours since he had heard Tino battering on the door with his paws. He wished now he had the dog with him. Every step was growing more difficult—his head felt on fire and he ached all over. Suddenly he knew that he had plague.

"Well, why not me as well as anyone else," he said to himself calmly, and because he could go no farther he crept into a wayside hut which had once been used to shelter cattle. And there he lay down with his staff beside him.

It was there, two days later, that Tino found him. How, no one could ever know, nor how the dog had escaped from the house. But he did, and although barely conscious, Roque felt the comfort of a warm lick on his face, and heard the short, sharp yap of joy Tino gave on finding him. Then the dog was off like an arrow from a bow.

"Alas," murmured Roque, "now I have no comfort at all."

He tried to pray, but the words got all mixed up in his fevered mind, until at last sleep came to him. When he opened his eyes the first thing they lighted upon was Tino, curled up beside him.

"So you came back, you rascal," he whispered.

Tino beat his tail upon the ground, then leapt up to draw attention to something he seemed very proud of. Roque followed the dog's movements languidly, wondering what it was all about. He felt a little better and, strangely enough, hungry. But what was the use of that? Not so much as a crumb could be lying about in this mud hovel.

But there was more than a crumb. Tino had seen to it that there was a whole newly-baked loaf! It was lying in a linen bag which was tied by a stout tape. No doubt the kindly baker had guessed the errand of mercy the little

dog was bent upon, and made it easy for him to carry it out.

"Oh, Tino, what a splendid friend you are!" cried Roque, new strength coming to him now he was not all alone. He knew enough about his sickness to be sure the worst of it was past. Now there would only be weakness —and maybe some starvation—for one loaf would not last long.

But Tino saw to it that when that one was nearly finished another took its place. And soon, not only did he haul along the loaf, but also the baker with it. He had him well gripped by his apron.

The man was laughing when he came into the hut.

"That dog of yours," he cried, "really he must be made the next Mayor of Piacenza! He has the brains and the tough spirit. When he came to my bakery nothing would do but that I should give him the loaf as usual. First of all he barked. That was nothing strange in a dog. Being a bit shorter than usual of bread, I took no notice of the racket he was making, but when he fell quiet I turned to look, and there he was, nosing a newly-baked loaf off the tray. I threw my sandal at him, but he held on to his bread. And I began to think that you, Signor, might be in great need of it. So I took one of my linen bags, and packed the loaf up, so that it might not be soiled on the way. Then I tried to fasten the bag round his neck, but

he would have none of that! I could not persuade him
that I wasn't going to take the bread from him. And
away he went!"

"Indeed he did," agreed Roque, smiling weakly. Now
that the fever had left him his limbs felt like jelly.

"But just wait to hear the rest," continued the baker.
"Did a loaf a day content that dog? No! As well as the
bread he wished for the baker! So here I am—and I see
why. He's a wonder of a dog, Signor, a marvel, a miracle!
And seeing you are better, I'm going to get him to allow me
to bring my cart and take you into my own home."

"How good you are," said Roque gratefully. "I might so
easily have died of hunger if not of plague."

"It's your dog you have to thank," replied the baker,
"because he found you when no one else had even looked.
You see, it's like this, Signor. In these days—with this
evil of a sickness in the town—folk just go out and don't
come back. The way our good priest did."

"Ah, yes," put in Roque sorrowfully, "I had gone in
search of him, when I myself fell by the wayside."

"But he's come back," said the baker cheerfully. "He
had a little mishap—fell into a small ravine. Lucky the
wolves didn't sniff him out. It seems he was carrying
some food to a family who are sheltering in the higher
part of the forest. So the good man didn't die of hunger.
And now he is seeking you. I can tell him you're all right,

owing to your dog. Now what a capital creature that is!"

Tino wagged his tail to show he understood all this praise, but his eyes never left his master's face. They seemed to say, "Wherever you had hidden yourself, I should have found you."

"The people are calling you a saint already," said the baker, pausing in the entrance to the hut as he moved off to go and get the cart.

Roque shook his head.

"They mustn't do that," he murmured. "I've done so little to help them, really. Why, this faithful dog has given as much service as any man."

The baker considered this, and then made answer thoughtfully. "His part won't be forgotten, either. You mark my words, Signor, long, long after our day—when all this trouble is forgotten—something will be remembered, something told again, and that will be the story of Saint Roque and his dog."

VISION GLORIOUS

THE time was near sunset and the air was full of the sound of little bells, for the goats were being driven down from the hills in case a wolf should come in the night. The steep and stony path which led down into the valley was misty with dust cast up by the hooves of the flock, behind which trudged three children—two boys and a little girl.

They had been on a visit to a married sister, and because Catherine, the little girl, could not walk very fast—especially when she was so tired—they were late getting home. Stefano, the elder of the two boys, kept calling out to her as she lagged behind, "Oh, hurry up, Catherine. How you dawdle! We shall find all the best bits eaten up when we reach home!"

Then she would mend her pace a bit, trotting beside

the boys, only to fall behind again. And it was not only because she was weary and footsore, but also because there was so much to look at.

Across the valley she could see the great stone walls of the Abbey Church of San Domenico, every window with its pointed arches gleaming gold in the last rays of the sun. Above the roof of the church the sky was deeply blue, with great splashes of rosy light spreading out like the petals of a flower.

Little Catherine's eyes grew bright with pleasure, as they always did when they saw anything beautiful. She forgot she was tired and hungry, forgot she was going home, until again Stefano called out, "Was there ever such a little snail? If you don't mend your paces I'll run on without you. Then maybe the wolf will come snuffing along thinking, 'Here's a nice morsel!' "

"I wouldn't be afraid of the wolf," said Catherine stoutly.

"Ho, ho!" jeered Stefano, "then would the wolf be afraid of you?"

"He might be," replied the little girl, "until he found out I meant no harm."

This made both the boys laugh, but Catherine was quite serious. She had never seen a wolf, but she had heard of St. Francis of Assisi, who had such a loving way with all God's creatures that the fiercest animals grew tame when he spoke to them.

"Well, let us hear what you would say to the wolf," teased Stefano.

She thought for a moment or two, then said slowly, "I should say, 'Now, be a good wolf. Don't frighten the goats on the hill-side, and be gentle and friendly to all. Then, every night I'll pray for you.'"

"Oh, Catherine, you do think of the oddest things," said Stefano, and he looked rather uncomfortable. However, remembering that supper was waiting and that he was hungry, he ran on with the other boy.

But Catherine did not hurry. She wanted to watch the great glowing ball of the sun go down behind the hills on the other side of the valley. The sun was in no hurry either. Brighter and brighter grew the sky to the west, more brilliant the windows of the church, and of a deeper blue the sky above it.

"Heaven is just beyond that bright sky," thought Catherine, and it was then she saw the vision.

It seemed to her that a picture was being painted on the sky above the roof of the Abbey Church. At first it looked something like those castles which appear and vanish in the heart of a bright red fire. But as she gazed in wonder and delight, the picture did not vanish but grew clearer, taking on forms and shapes until, dazzled by its shining beauty, she realized that she was seeing a vision of the Saviour of the World, sitting upon a royal throne and wearing regal robes, a triple crown upon His

head. All the sweetness and light of divine love lit up
His face, and to Catherine—watching almost spellbound
there—it seemed as if His smile was especially for her. It
seemed to go right into her heart, which it filled with a
joy so great that she pressed her hand to her side to still
its throb. And still the picture grew.

And now she could see the apostles St. Peter and St.
Paul standing beside Him. In his hands St. Peter carried
the keys of Heaven. He looked old and kind, but St.
Paul, who was carrying the Holy Writ, was strong and
grave. There, also, close to the Saviour's right hand,
knelt the disciple He loved the best of all, St. John the
Evangelist.

The child stood transfixed, and through her wide, dark
eyes took in, not only the beauty of what she saw, but also
its message. And again it seemed to her that the King of
Heaven smiled lovingly upon her, then lifted His hand
to bless her with the Sign of the Cross. At that moment
she knew He claimed her to do His work in the world.
Her lips moved. "I will be good," she whispered, and
although Stefano was again urging her to come home,
she only put up her hand, as if to ward off anything that
might come between her and the vow she was making to
the Light of the World.

"Catherine, Catherine!" the shrill, earthly voice teased
and distressed her, and because she wanted to stay where

she was until that marvel in the sky had faded she burst into tears. But she did not move. Then Stefano ran back, and taking her by the arm, tried to pull her along. But she dug her toes into the ground, resisting him with all her strength, the tears running like little rivulets down her cheeks.

"Whatever is the matter with you?" he asked. "And why are you crying?"

She did not answer, but sighed as if waking from a dream and pointed to the fading colors of the sky. Stefano stared, but saw nothing but the last of the sunset.

"Look, look, over the roof of the church!" she said at last.

"There's nothing there but sky," he grumbled.

She had no words to describe her vision. All she could say was, "If only you could have seen what I saw, you never would have called me away from so sweet a sight. But now it has faded—I have lost it."

And she began to weep again.

"Little sister, you are very tired and very hungry," said Stefano gently, "and that is why you think you see things which really are not there."

At this, the tears dried on her cheeks and she turned on him with great spirit to reply, "Not there! What I saw was more real than this street, or the people walking along it. Oh, what you missed when you ran on! If you had not been in such a hurry you might have shared with me something to make you happy all your life long!"

"And yet you cannot tell me what it was?" asked Stefano, taking her hand.

She shook her head and sighed.

"No, it was too wonderful for words," she replied, and did not speak again until she saw her mother standing on the doorstep waiting for them anxiously, shading her eyes with her hand.

"How late you are!" their mother called out; then added cheerfully, "but what a wonderful sunset! I've never seen one quite like it. I hope it is a good omen."

"Catherine almost fell into a trance watching it," said Stefano. "I told her a wolf would be after her if she kept supper waiting too long."

"Now, you're not to frighten her with tales of that kind," scolded his mother. "She's only six, you know."

"Frightened!" laughed Stefano. "She wasn't frightened! Not a bit. She said she'd talk to the wolf the way St. Francis did."

"There's a bold girl!" The mother laughed, too, before saying more seriously, "But you mustn't place yourself with the saints, my girl. That's presumptuous. They are given special powers from Heaven to act as they do."

Catherine said nothing. But in her heart she knew that she—a little girl, the child of humble people, and herself still untaught—had, as she stood there waiting for the sun to set, been given special powers to work—even if in the most lowly fashion—in the service of God. She had been chosen, and now must begin at once to fit herself to be worthy.

From that time her parents noticed that she played less and prayed more, but all the same was the gayest and happiest of the family, and never so happy as when at the hour of sunset—the air full of the sound of little bells— she stood and looked across the valley to where above the roof of the Abbey Church she had seen "The Vision Glorious."

NOTES ON THE SAINTS

St. Jerome

St. Jerome, the most famous of the Latin Fathers, was born in Dalmatio (now a part of Yugoslavia) about A.D. 340. He went to Rome for his higher education, and was there baptized. At the age of about thirty he went to Antioch, and then spent four years as a desert hermit, practicing religious austerities and studying Hebrew. Ordained priest, he went to Constantinople, and thence on a mission to Rome, where he was secretary to Pope Damasus. He became famous as an eloquent and learned preacher, and worked at revising the old Latin version of the Bible.

A visit to Egypt put him in touch with more of sacred learning, and he visited the chief monasteries. But the Holy Land called him, and in 385 he settled at Bethlehem. There he not only continued his work of revising the Bible, but also wrote such violent attacks against various heretics that his life was in danger. So he left Bethlehem and went into hiding until 418. He lived only two years after his return, dying in 420.

The first editor of his collected works was the great scholar, Erasmus. His Latin version of the Scriptures was the foundation of the Vulgate (i.e., the popular edition), which was pronounced "authentic" by the Council of Trent in the middle of the sixteeth century.

St. Patrick

Patrick was the son of a romanized Briton, a decurion (municipal councillor) in Holy Orders, and was probably born in South Wales. The date of his birth is uncertain; but there is no doubt that he lived in the fifth century. At the age of sixteen he was captured by pirates who often attacked the Welsh coast, and was sold to a chief of Antrim. He served as a swineherd for six years or so, until he managed to escape, eventually reaching France. There he became a monk and resided at the monastery of Lerins (an island close to Cannes). In time he was ordained priest and returned to Ireland.

Landing at Wicklow, he made his way north to County Down, where he converted Dichu, Lord of the Soil. Through Dichu he was enabled to build his first church, at Saul, close to Downpatrick. Thenceforward his mission was marked by energy and success. He preached to the High King at Tara, traveled over much of Ireland, baptized converts, and founded monasteries. He may, in the year 440 or 441, have visited Rome and received the papal blessing. Finally, he fixed his see at Armagh, from which he seems to have issued decrees. He died at Saul, and was buried at Downpatrick. The date of his death, like that of his birth, is much disputed.

We have two genuine writings from his pen, in rather crude Latin. The most important is his *Confession,* an autobiography more spiritual than factual, which often leaves us guessing. The other, a letter to Caroticus, a pirate who had carried off some of his followers, reveals the saint's essential nobility. In St. John Gogarty's *I Follow Saint Patrick* there is a complete translation of the *Confession.*

It has been said that St. Patrick monopolized Ireland, and that Ireland monopolized Patrick. But there is more to him than that. When the power and civilization of Rome were dying in dark chaos, the monasteries of Ireland built up a culture which was unique in Europe. From them came forth a stream of saints and missionaries who carried their culture to England and Northern Europe, while the monks who stayed behind kept alive the study of the great classics.

ST. BRIDGET

St. Bridget (or Bride) is reputed to have been born of a princely family, early in the fifth century, and to have come at an early age under the direct teaching of St. Patrick, who converted her to Christianity. Joined by other women of her new Faith, she formed a religious community, which branched out into various nunneries in every part of Ireland. Each of these acknowledged her as its Abbess and spiritual head. In all the stories and legends about her, St. Bridget appears as a woman of great courage, wit, and charm, whose wide cloak of celestial blue gained her one of the many titles she is known by—Brigid of the Mantle, The Fair Maid of February, St. Bride of the Kindly Fire, and others. In Scotland, where her influence was as potent as in her native Ireland, women would invoke her blessings on the new-born babe, while shepherds on the hillside sought her goodwill for the early lambs. Her emblems, the first yellow flowers of spring, the lamb, and the sea-bird, have given rise to more romantic stories and poems than surround the name of any other saint, unless it be St. Francis of Assisi, with whom she is linked in the saintly legends, as being a lover of everything that God has made. Tradition tells us that St. Bridget was buried in one grave with St. Patrick and St. Columba at Downpatrick Cathedral, County Down.

An old distich runs:

These three rest in one tomb in Down,
Brigid, Patrick, and pious Columba.

St. Ciaran

St. Ciaran (pronounced Kiaran) was a famous Irish saint whose love, both of his fellow men and of animals, reminds us of St. Francis of Assisi. Born in north Ireland, he first settled on Hare Island in Lough Ree, north of Athlone, to which he is said to have been guided by a stag. But he is best remembered by his foundation of the abbey of Clonmacnois (on the Shannon, to the south of Athlone). This was in 541, about 100 years after St. Patrick had fixed his see at Armagh. The ruins of the seven churches there made it one of the holiest places in Ireland, and the festival of St. Ciaran on 9th September attracted great crowds of pilgrims. The fame of the saint and the spirit of his work spread throughout Ireland. But his life was all too brief, for he died at Clonmacnois in 549 in his thirty-third year.

St. Margaret of Scotland

The life of St. Margaret, who was born about 1045, was passed amid some of the most disturbed years of Britain's history. She was the daughter of the Atheling (Prince) Edward, and was thus the grand-daughter of Edmund Ironside. Her mother was Hungarian, of noble or perhaps royal family, and Margaret herself seems to have been born in Hungary. When Duke William of Normandy made himself master of England, Margaret, with her family, sought flight by sea. The ship was driven ashore on the Scottish coast at a place which still bears the name of St. Margaret's Hope, not far from the Forth Bridge.

The Scottish King, Malcolm Canmore, the son of King Duncan (who was murdered by Macbeth), was, like many of the Scots nobility, a rough, fierce man, but with an underlying generosity. Margaret was beautiful, and of a refined type, which was new to him. Their marriage in 1069 enabled her to introduce a touch of civilization and to bring the Celtic Church, which had been founded by St. Patrick, into line with continental practice. She herself built a fine church at the royal town of Dunfermline, and she restored the ruined shrine of Iona, which had suffered so cruelly at the hands of the Norsemen. Though she won the hearts of most of her subjects, some of them resented the fact that all her children were given Saxon names. (Malcolm had spent some years at the Saxon Court.)

But Scotland and England were continually at war, and raid and counter-raid were almost incessant, till Malcolm was forced to render homage to the Norman. In 1093, when William Rufus had succeeded to the throne, Malcolm and his eldest son were trapped and killed by the Earl of Northumberland. Three days later Margaret herself died.

She had six sons, three of whom, in turn, succeeded to the Scottish throne. Margaret herself did much to help the development of Scotland by welcoming the English refugees who fled from the Conqueror's terrible "Harrowing of the North." Her example of a fine type of Christianity left her memory fragrant through the centuries. Her daughter Elizabeth ("Matilda") married Henry I of England.

She was canonized in 1250.

St. Francis

Francis was born at Assisi (one of the picturesque hill towns of Central Italy) in 1182. His father was a prosperous cloth merchant. Francis, after an early life of careless gaiety, became a soldier and was taken prisoner by the Perugians. When peace brought his release, he became seriously ill. His meditations during his illness gradually led him to his great decision—to carry out literally the teaching of the Gospels and to give up his wealth and gay life. Even his father's violent opposition had no effect in deterring him.

He retreated to the half-ruined chapel of St. Damian near Assisi, and before long began to preach. Followers soon flocked to him, and from these he founded his Franciscan Order, with its vows of chastity, poverty, and obedience. His followers did not beg for their food, for Francis always insisted on the necessity of work. In 1216 the Franciscans sought and won the approval of Pope Innocent III for their Order.

Francis visited North Africa, Spain, Syria, and even Egypt, where, though he failed to convert the Sultan, he won kinder treatment for Christian captives. His last few years were spent in Italy, saddened by the divisions which had already grown up in his Order, largely because many of his follwers could not live up to the way of life he had initiated. He died in 1226, and was canonized in 1228.

The well-known *Little Flowers* was put together from a Latin original nearly a century after Francis' death. In this are such stories as the "Wolf of Gubbio" and of the Saint preaching to the birds. The *Mirror of Perfection* was put together only a few years earlier.

St. Bartholomew

St. Bartholomew of Dunelm (or of Farne as he is sometimes called) was a monk of the abbey of Durham who became famous for his piety and for the sanctity of his life. As with other such holy men, miracles were freely attributed to him. He lived in the twelfth century and died about 1193.

He must not be confused with his better known name-sake, the Apostle.

St. Elizabeth of Hungary

Elizabeth, daughter of Andreas II, King of Hungary, was born at Presburg in 1207. At the age of four she was betrothed to Duke Ludwig IV of Thuringia in Western Germany, and was taken to his Court to be brought up as his future consort.

From this early age—like Catherine of Siena—she felt a compelling urge to live the religious life and carry out the teaching of Christ. She showed no liking for princely pomp, but began, even as a child, to practice self-mortification and benevolence to others, especially to the poor.

Married at the age of fourteen, she became the mother of a boy and two girls. Though the Duke admired her saintly way of life, the Court hinted that she would be better suited to a convent.

About six years after her marriage the Duke took the Crusader's cross, but he died at Otranto just as he was about to embark to join the Emperor Barbarossa. Elizabeth was soon driven out by a brutal brother-in-law, and she suffered great hardship. She was rescued by an aunt, an abbess, who took her into her monastery.

When her husband's warriors returned from Palestine she was restored to her rights and granted a revenue, the whole of which she devoted to the relief of the poor. At the hospital which she founded she worked as a nurse, undertaking the most unpleasant tasks, such as tending the lepers. She died in 1231, when she was only twenty-four.

Many miracles are attributed to her, and in 1236 the fine church which bears her name was built at Marburg.

ST. ROQUE

St. Roque (or Roche) is said to have been born at Montpellier in Languedoc about 1295. His father, who was governor of the city, was of noble birth.

At an early age the boy showed his sympathy with the sufferings of his fellow creatures, and this may have led him to study medicine so that he might be more fitted to heal the sick.

When he was about twenty he set off on a pilgrimage to Rome; but he stopped on the way to attend to victims of the plague which was raging in parts of Italy. He caught the infection and, according to the traditional story, would have died had not his faithful dog brought him food.

The "facts" of St. Roque's life seem to depend upon the *Golden Legend,* a very uncritical collection of stories. The only certain date connected with him is that of the Council of Constance in 1414, at which there was mention of his noble life.

After his early death, he was venerated afresh whenever plague broke out. A church in Venice was built in his honor, and his effigy was carried through the streets as a protection against the dread disease.

Milburn, in *Saints and Their Emblems,* dates his activity in combating the plague "about 1350."

ST. CATHERINE OF SIENA

Catherine, the child of a wool-dyer, had the unusual position of being the youngest of a family of twenty-five. She is often said to have been born in 1347, but recent research makes 1334 more probable.

Her vision, at the age of six, affected the whole of her subsequent life. She not only displayed the qualities of sainthood attributed to many other saints, such as mystical ecstasies, the ability to exist on a minimum of food and sleep, and the appearance of Stigmata (marks corresponding to Christ's wounds), but she also became a person of power in the troubled history of her time.

Those were the days of the "Great Schism," when for some seventy years the Popes had been in exile at Avignon (where the great Papal Palace still stands by the Rhône). Catherine made the long and dangerous journey to persuade Gregory XI to return to Rome. With great courage she rebuked the sins of the Papal Court, and sent the Pope back by sea to Rome—an achievement which has been compared to the self-imposed mission of Joan of Arc.

When Urban VI became Pope in 1378 Catherine fought for him against the anti-pope and the French cardinals, though she failed to end the Great Schism before she died.

Catherine also brought the quarrel between the people of Florence and the Pope to a peaceful end, and she effected many reforms in the Dominican order, to which she belonged.

She died—worn out by her labors and austerities—in 1380, a unique figure in the Calendar of Saints.